Mommy and Me

How I Came to Be

(A Mommy & Child Family Story)

Elizabeth R. Weiss

Brave Bold Mamas Publication

Dedicated to

All the brave, strong, single mamas and their profoundly loved little ones

My children, without whom I would never have known such indescribable love and this amazing journey of motherhood

FIRST EDITION

Brave Bold Mamas Publication

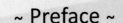

~ Preface ~

My hope in creating this book is for it to be a tool that supports you in teaching your little one about different families and each child's individual story. This book is designed to help you forge conversations. It does not delve into the terminology of anatomy and conception nor fertility methods. This is intentional, allowing you to select the wording with which you are most comfortable for your family and child's age. As you share this story with your little one, you may wish to add additional details and use this book as a foundation for more in-depth conversations.

Hi, I'm Cole!

Ever wonder how you came to be
- like how did you get here?

How did you get into your
mommy's tummy, and things like
that?

I know my mommy wanted to have a
baby to love and care for, to hug
and hold, to teach and watch grow!

She told me that some people have babies easily, the first time they try. And some people work very hard to have a baby and try, and try, and try many times.

Either way, every story is unique and special about how a baby came to be.

I have two important things to tell you about how I came to be.

FIRST: When a mommy is ready to make a baby, she needs a little help.

She may have a special man in her life to help, and he may become the daddy.

Or, with the help of a doctor, a mommy can get help from another kind of special man called a donor.

A donor is a person who wants to help someone have a baby and provides the part a mommy needs.

My mommy looked and looked for the right donor to help make a special baby who was just perfect for her.

While my mommy and I don't know the name of our donor, we know he must be a pretty special person since he wanted to help a mommy do something as amazing as having a baby.

So, with the help of the doctor, and the help of the donor, my mommy got to have me!

She carried me around in her belly for a long time while I grew, and grew, and grew.

She felt me growing bigger and bigger, and even felt some kicks and somersaults from me inside her belly!

Finally, the special day arrived. After all of her planning and waiting, the baby she always dreamed of finally arrived - ME!

SECOND thing to know: When a mommy has a baby this way (with the help of a donor), there usually isn't a daddy. But there is soooo much love from my mommy, who worked so hard to have me!

And there are lots and lots of people who love me . . .
like my grandparents, aunts, uncles, cousins, close friends,
and so many others!! *So much love!*

I know kids with many different kinds of families. If I'm asked if I have a daddy, I say "No, we are a Mommy & Kid family!"

(When I was younger, I said we were a Mommy & Baby family.)

Some kids have a mommy and a daddy in the same house, some have a mommy and a daddy in different houses. Some kids have stepmoms, stepdads, two mommies, or two daddies. Some kids might have only a daddy, or have an aunt, uncle, or a grandma in the house . . . .

No matter who makes up your family, it's *alllll* good!

Family. Love. Support. That's what matters! 🩶

My mommy wanted me so much that she had me all by herself. Isn't that cool?

She loves me soooo much!!!

Thank you to my dear mommy friends for your input, support, and solidarity – especially Meghan Melore, Lori Bongiorno, and Leah Samji

Cover and background design, character enhancements, and formatting by Sunil Nissanka Amarasinghe

If you enjoyed this book, please consider writing a review on Amazon or your online bookseller of choice. Thank you!

Made in the USA
Monee, IL
08 November 2020